THE GREAT BIBLE
DISCOVERY

SAMUEL AND SAUL

THE BIBLE IS A BEST-SELLER. IT IS ALSO ONE OF THE MASTER-WORKS OF WORLD LITERATURE - SO IMPORTANT THAT UNIVERSITIES TODAY TEACH 'NON-RELIGIOUS' BIBLE COURSES TO HELP STUDENTS WHO CHOOSE TO STUDY WESTERN LITERATURE.

THE BIBLE POSSESSES AN AMAZING POWER TO FASCINATE YOUNG AND OLD ALIKE.

ONE REASON FOR THIS UNIVERSAL APPEAL IS THAT IT DEALS WITH BASIC HUMAN LONGINGS, EMOTIONS, RELATIONSHIPS. 'ALL THE WORLD IS HERE.' ANOTHER REASON IS THAT SO MUCH OF THE BIBLE CONSISTS OF STORIES. THEY ARE FULL OF MEANING BUT EASY TO REMEMBER.

HERE ARE THOSE STORIES, PRESENTED SIMPLY AND WITH A MINIMUM OF EXPLANATION. WE HAVE LEFT THE TEXT TO SPEAK FOR ITSELF. GIFTED ARTISTS USE THE ACTION-STRIP TECHNIQUE TO BRING THE BIBLE'S DEEP MESSAGE TO READERS OF ALL AGES. THEIR DRAWINGS ARE BASED ON INFORMATION FROM ARCHAEOLOGICAL DISCOVERIES COVERING FIFTEEN CENTURIES.

AN ANCIENT BOOK - PRESENTED FOR THE PEOPLE OF THE SECOND MILLENNIUM. A RELIGIOUS BOOK - PRESENTED FREE FROM THE INTERPRETATION OF ANY PARTICULAR CHURCH. A UNIVERSAL BOOK - PRESENTED IN A FORM THAT ALL MAY ENJOY.

OM publishing
CARLISLE, UK

7

The story of little Samuel, asleep in the Temple and awoken by the voice of the Lord, is one of the most appealing in the Old Testament. But when he grew up Samuel was one of the most important leaders in Israel's history. As the Temple story reminds us, he was a prophet , who heard God's voice and acted as his messenger. He was also the last of the judges - he judged disputes, he united the people in loyalty to the Lord and in resisting the enemy. It was Samuel who appointed their first king - their first two kings, to be precise.

It was the threat from the Philistines that led the Hebrews to ask for a king. About the same time as the Hebrews invaded from the east, the Philistines had arrived in Palestine. (Canaan became known as 'Palestine' because the Philistines lived there.) They settled along the coast but began to advance inland, where they came into conflict with the Hebrews. The Philistines were better equipped and better organized. The Hebrews felt they needed a full-time king to lead them. Nobody knew, after all, when or where the Lord would raise up a judge. It would be better to have a king, like other nations.

The whole point of being Israel, however , was that you were not like other nations. Saul was singled out in several ways - by Samuel's prophecy, by casting lots, and finally by delivering the town of Jabesh.

Saul had a great deal going for him. But he disobeyed God's message through Samuel and he also tried to act as a priest by offering sacrifice. No Hebrew king was supposed to claim priestly as well as royal authority since this would have made him too powerful. Naturally some did, but the consequences were harmful. Saul became moody and irritable. He died by his own hand. David, who succeeded him, had a very different personality. He was popular and - as people say of successful politicians and generals - 'lucky'. The killing of Goliath was typical of the way things used to work out right for David. The Bible says that 'the Lord was with him'.

1 Samuel

Deuteronomy 17:15-20

SAMUEL AND SAUL

First published as *Découvrir la Bible* 1983

First edition © Librairie Larousse 1983

24-volume series adaptation by Mike Jacklin © Knowledge Unlimited 1994
This edition © OM Publishing 1995

01 00 99 98 97 96 95   7 6 5 4 3 2 1

OM Publishing is an imprint of Send the Light Ltd.,
P.O. Box 300, Carlisle, Cumbria CA3 0QS, U.K.

Introductions: Peter Cousins

British Library Cataloguing in Publication Data
A catalogue record for this book is available from the British Library
ISBN 1-85078-211-3

Printed in Singapore by Tien Wah Press (Pte) Ltd.

AS THEY DID EVERY YEAR, ELKANAH AND HIS TWO WIVES WERE GOING TO WORSHIP AT SHILOH, WHERE THE COVENANT BOX WAS KEPT.

SAMUEL AND SAUL

SCENARIO: Etienne DAHLER
DRAWING: Pierre FRISANO

THIS TIME YOU CAN ASK GOD FOR SOMETHING ELSE INSTEAD OF A CHILD!

HANNAH, YOU'LL NEVER HAVE ANY CHILDREN!

PENINNAH, THAT'S ENOUGH!

PEOPLE CAME FROM ALL OVER THE LAND TO SHILOH FOR SUKKOTH, THE FESTIVAL OF SHELTERS.

3

WHEN THE CHILD WAS WEANED, HANNAH TOOK HIM TO SHILOH. SHE OFFERED A SACRIFICE, THEN WENT BACK TO ELI.

SIR, THIS IS THE CHILD I PRAYED FOR. I'LL LEAVE HIM WITH YOU, SO HE CAN SERVE GOD ALL HIS LIFE.

SAMUEL STAYED WITH ELI, TO SERVE IN THE SHRINE.

ELI'S TWO SONS WERE ALSO PRIESTS, BUT THEY BEHAVED VERY BADLY... THEY SHARED THE OFFERINGS GIVEN TO THE SHRINE WITH THEIR SERVANTS.

ELI'S TOO SOFT WITH HIS SONS. THEY'LL COME TO A BAD END!

GOD CAN'T BE MOCKED LIKE THIS.

5

IN THE PHILISTINE CAMP...

THEY'VE BROUGHT THEIR GOD TO THEIR CAMP!

WE'RE LOST! HE RESCUED THEM FROM THE EGYPTIANS!

COURAGE! DON'T BE AFRAID OF A BOX THEY THINK IS HOLY! WE'RE GOING TO BEAT THEM!

THAT DAY MANY ISRAELITE SOLDIERS WERE KILLED, AND THE PHILISTINES CAPTURED THE COVENANT BOX.

ALL THE ISRAELITES WERE PLUNGED INTO DESPAIR BY THIS TERRIBLE NEWS... AND IN HIS GRIEF OLD ELI DIED.

TWENTY YEARS WENT BY... THE ISRAELITES FORGOT THE COVENANT BOX, TURNED AWAY FROM GOD, AND WORSHIPPED IDOLS.

A GROUP OF ELDERS WENT TO SAMUEL...

SAMUEL, YOU'RE THE ONLY PERSON IN ISRAEL WHO CAN DELIVER US FROM THE PHILISTINES.

NO! T ALL DEPENDS ON OU! DESTROY YOUR DOLS, AND TURN BACK TO THE LORD... HE'LL SAVE YOU.

NOW GATHER ALL THE PEOPLE TOGETHER AT MIZPAH... I'LL PRAY TO THE LORD FOR YOU.

THE PHILISTINES HEARD THE NEWS...

SURROUND THEM WHILE THEY'RE PRAYING! THEN ATTACK THEM!

TWO YEARS LATER...

SAUL! SAUL! I'VE TERRIBLE NEWS FOR YOU!

NAHASH THE AMMONITE IS BESIEGING THE TOWN OF JABESH. IF ITS PEOPLE GIVE THEMSELVES UP, HE'LL SPARE THEIR LIVES...

...BUT HE'LL PUT OUT EVERYONE'S RIGHT EYE AS A SIGN OF SLAVERY!

SAUL WAS SO ANGRY THAT HE KILLED HIS OXEN AND CUT THEM IN PIECES.

HE WANTS TO INFLICT THIS DISGRACE ON THE WHOLE OF ISRAEL!

VERY WELL! THEN NAHASH WILL HAVE TO DEFEAT THE WHOLE OF ISRAEL!

GO AND TELL THEM IN EPHRAIM THAT THIS WILL HAPPEN TO THEIR BEASTS IF THEY DON'T JOIN ME IN THIS CAMPAIGN!

WHEN THEY CAME BACK FROM EPHRAIM...

SAUL, WE HAVE A THOUSAND MEN.

FINE! WE'LL ATTACK AT DAYBREAK TOMORROW.

SURPRISED BY THE ATTACK, THE AMMONITES WERE DEFEATED AND R... AWAY.

18

OUR COMMANDER HAS BEEN KILLED!

IN TIME SAUL HAD A PERMANENT ARMY. ONE DAY HIS SON JONATHAN ATTACKED THE PHILISTINES...

THE NEWS MADE THE PHILISTINES SO FURIOUS THAT THEY GATHERED TO FIGHT THE ISRAELITES.

MANY ISRAELITES TOOK FRIGHT AND RAN AWAY TO THE MOUNTAINS OR ACROSS THE JORDAN. AT GILGAL SAUL SPOKE TO THE ANXIOUS CROWD.

DON'T BE AFRAID! GOD IS SENDING SAMUEL TO OFFER A SACRIFICE.

WELL, THEN I'LL OFFER THE SACRIFICE MYSELF...

SAUL, THE PROPHET SAMUEL IS TAKING TOO LONG... HE SAID SEVEN DAYS... THE PHILISTINES ARE GOING TO ATTACK US...

WHAT HAVE YOU DONE? GOD APPOINTED ME TO OFFER SACRIFICES.

UNDERSTAND THIS SAUL: YOU REJECT GOD'S COMMAND; NOW GOD REJECT YOU. HE'S ALREA LOOKING FOR SOMEONE TO TAKE YOUR PLACE.

JUST AS SAUL FINISHED OFFERING THE SACRIFICE, SAMUEL ARRIVED...

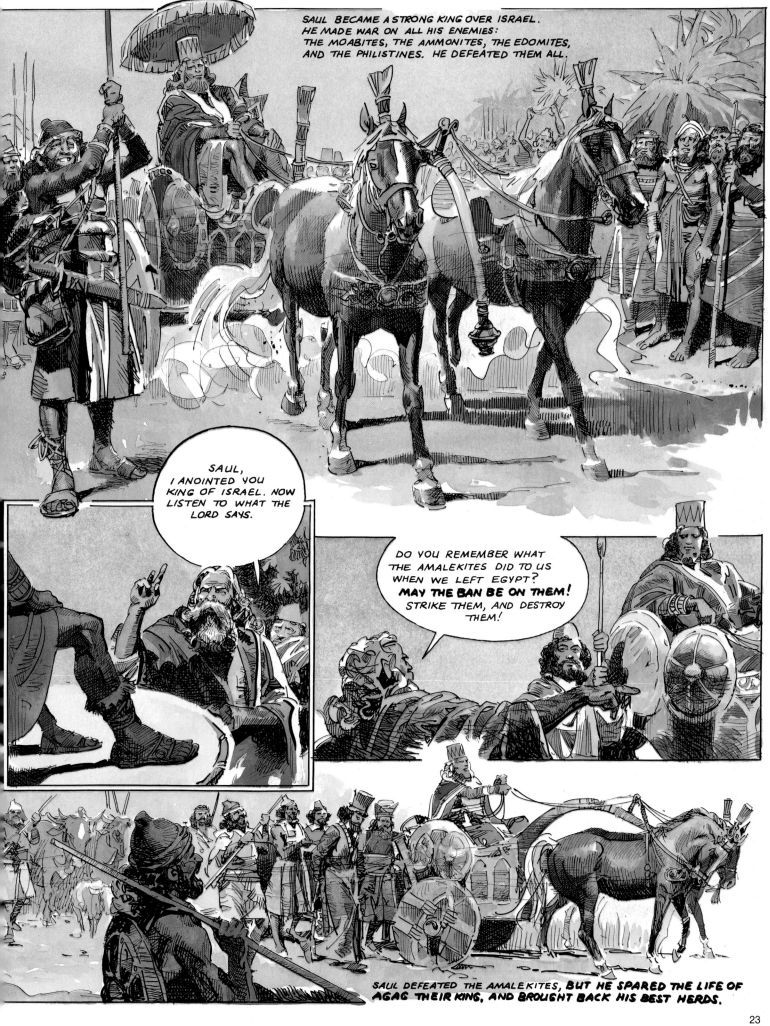

SAUL BECAME A STRONG KING OVER ISRAEL. HE MADE WAR ON ALL HIS ENEMIES: THE MOABITES, THE AMMONITES, THE EDOMITES, AND THE PHILISTINES. HE DEFEATED THEM ALL.

SAUL, I ANOINTED YOU KING OF ISRAEL. NOW LISTEN TO WHAT THE LORD SAYS.

DO YOU REMEMBER WHAT THE AMALEKITES DID TO US WHEN WE LEFT EGYPT? **MAY THE BAN BE ON THEM!** STRIKE THEM, AND DESTROY THEM!

SAUL DEFEATED THE AMALEKITES, BUT HE SPARED THE LIFE OF AGAG THEIR KING, AND BROUGHT BACK HIS BEST HERDS.

SAMUEL WENT BACK TO RAMAH.
UNTIL THE DAY HE DIED,
HE NEVER AGAIN SAW SAUL.

DAVID

SCENARIO: Etienne DAHLER
DRAWING: Paolo ELEUTERI-SERPIERI

DAVID, COME BACK TO THE HOUSE QUICKLY; THE PROPHET SAMUEL WANTS TO SEE YOU.

SAMUEL! AT OUR HOUSE?

HURRY UP, BROTHER! I'LL EXPLAIN AS WE GO.

31

THE TWO ARMIES DREW UP IN THE VALLEY OF ELAH.

IN THE PHILISTINE CAMP THE LEADERS MET...

WE'RE SURE TO WIN, SO WE DON'T NEED TO LOSE A LOT OF SOLDIERS. WE'VE CHOSEN YOU TO CHALLENGE ONE OF SAUL'S MEN TO SINGLE COMBAT...

I CHALLENGE THE ARMY OF ISRAEL TODAY. CHOOSE ONE OF YOUR MEN TO FIGHT ME.

THE MAN WENT OUT TO CONFRONT THE ISRAELITES.
HIS NAME WAS GOLIATH.

ON THE WAY BACK SAUL'S SOLDIERS LOOTED THE DESERTED PHILISTINE CAMP.

THE LORD HAS GIVEN YOU MANY TALENTS. YOU'RE JUST AS GOOD WITH THE SLING AS YOU ARE WITH THE HARP!

DAVID, YOU'LL BE SUCCESSFUL. I'LL KEEP YOU IN MY SERVICE.

DAVID, ACCEPT THESE GIFTS.

BUT, JONATHAN, YOU'RE A PRINCE OF ISRAEL, SAUL'S SON!

AND YOU'RE THE ONE GOD LOVES!

DAVID, DON'T STAY HERE! GO IN PEACE, FOR WE'VE SWORN BEFORE THE LORD TO BE FAITHFUL TO EACH OTHER.

DAVID LEFT QUICKLY WITH SOME MEN HE COULD TRUST. MICHAL BECAME THE WIFE OF ANOTHER MAN.

AT NOB HE WENT TO THE PRIEST AHIMELECH...

WE'RE ON THE KING'S BUSINESS, AND WE'VE HAD NOTHING TO EAT FOR THREE DAYS. DO YOU HAVE ANY BREAD TO GIVE US?

I'VE ONLY THE LOAVES DEDICATED TO GOD... BUT I'LL GO AND GET THEM.

DO YOU HAVE A SWORD TOO?

THE SWORD OF GOLIATH, WHOM YOU KILLED, IS HERE. TAKE THAT, IF YOU LIKE.

THEN DAVID SOUGHT REFUGE IN THE DESERT.

ONE DAY TWO MEN FROM KEILAH CAME TO FIND DAVID...

THE PHILISTINES HAVE SACKED OUR TOWN AND STOLEN OUR CROPS.

YOU'RE THE ONLY ONE WHO CAN HELP US!

DAVID WENT AWAY FOR SOME TIME TO PRAY TO THE LORD. WHEN HE CAME BACK...

WE'LL FOLLOW YOU!

DAVID DEFEATED THE PHILISTINES, TOOK BACK THE STOLEN CATTLE, AND SAVED THE TOWN OF KEILAH, WHERE HE STAYED FOR A TIME. **SAUL WAS FURIOUS...**

DAVID HAS MADE A MISTAKE IN SETTLING IN KEILAH. **I'LL BESIEGE THE TOWN.**

BY THE TIME SAUL GETS HERE, DAVID WILL BE FAR AWAY!

DAVID FLED TO THE DESERT OF MAON. CLOSE BY LIVED A VERY RICH MAN NAMED NABAL. DAVID HAD PROTECTED HIS SHEPHERDS AND FLOCKS AGAINST ROBBERS.

MASTER, DAVID NEEDS PROVISIONS...

LET HIM WORK FOR THEM! I'LL NO GIVE EVEN A CRUS OF BREAD TO THAT GANG OF GOOD-FOR-NOTHINGS!

NABAL PAYS ME BACK EVIL FOR GOOD!

SPARE NABAL! I'M ABIGAIL, HIS WIFE. FORGIVE HIM, AND ACCEPT THESE PRESENTS.

MAY GOD BLESS YOU, ABIGAIL! I WON'T HARM NABAL.

TEN DAYS LATER NABAL DIED. DAVID SENT FOR ABIGAIL AND MARRIED HER.

I'VE NOTHING TO OFFER YOU, YOU KNOW. SAMUEL'S DEAD, AND I'M A LOST DOG HUNTED DOWN IN THE DESERT.!

NO, DAVID! SOON YOU'LL BE KING!

SAUL FOUND OUT WHERE DAVID WAS HIDING. HE SET OFF IN PURSUIT WITH HIS BEST SOLDIERS. DAVID WENT TO MEET HIM.

YOU SEE SAUL'S TENT? IN THE MIDDLE! LET'S GO THERE QUICKLY!